I AM...PEOPLE

WRITTEN BY JOANNE MARXHAUSEN
ILLUSTRATED BY BENJAMIN MARXHAUSEN

CONCORDIA
PUBLISHING HOUSE
3558 SOUTH JEFFERSON AVENUE
SAINT LOUIS, MISSOURI 63118

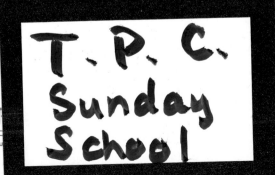

To God
who made people

Library of Congress Cataloging in Publication Data

Marxhausen, Joanne
   I am People.

     SUMMARY: The reader tries to imagine the feelings and experiences of all people.

     [1. Christian life -- Fiction]
I. Marxhausen, Benjamin II. Title

PZ7.M3684I af   [E]   78-12755

I AM PEOPLE

Copyright © 1979 by Concordia Publishing House
3558 So. Jefferson Avenue, St. Louis, MO 63118

Library of Congress Catalog Card Number:
ISBN 0-570-07953-5

Printed in the United States of America

WHAT THE BOOK IS ALL ABOUT:

This book is one of a series of books, which attempts to involve the reader in a journey to finding himself. It does so by arousing the reader's eagerness to learn more about God's creation, including himself, and by leading him onto the road of continuing quest for knowledge of God's creation through observation, through study, and through search of God's Word. The books offer opportunity for the reader to lose himself in this quest, for giving himself over to glorifying God in kinship with others of God's creatures, for sacrificing himself to whatever is God's plan for him in His Kingdom; and in so doing to really find himself.

As the reader travels through the books, getting better acquainted with one object after another of God's creation, studying the works of the great Master Creator (in whose image we are made), he may feel his own sense of creativity growing. Pages for creative writing and creative art are included as an outlet for this creativity. These activities are merely meant as a springboard for others.

Through this acquaintance with objects in God's creation, the reader is led into a meaningful relationship with those objects, with other people, with God, and with himself. Awareness is stimulated to depths of understanding and empathy. With such awareness appreciation can become a reality — appreciation not just for pleasantries, but appreciation which comes from knowing that God works all things together for good to those who love Him. Awareness and appreciation are keys that unlock us from ourselves and set us free to really live.

Happy journey!

What are people made of?
What color are they?
What shape are they?
Why are people?
What are people doing?
What are people to each other?
What are people needing?
What are people according to Romans 3:23?
How does God feel about all people (John 3:16)?
What are people able to do that no other
    creature can do?
What are people looking for?
What are people like according to
    Isaiah 40: 6-7?
What are people saying?
                    ...with their tongues?
                    ...with their eyes?
                    ...with their hands?
What are people listening to?
Where are people going?
How are people feeling?
What are people seeing?

People are . . .

Jesus said,
    "People are like sheep.
They go astray."

They need a shepherd to find them
            and to guide them
                    and protect them
                        and care for them.

People are... like rocks.

Sometimes they get kicked around.

Sometimes they are stumbling blocks
         to others.
Some people are living stones
    that build the kingdom of God.

People are... like trees.

They put down roots.
They branch out.
They bear fruit.
Some bear good fruit.
Some bear bad fruit.

A blind man was brought to Jesus that He should touch and heal him. Jesus touched the blind man's eyes, and the blind man said, "I see people, but they look like trees walking around." Then Jesus touched the blind man's eyes again, and the man said, "Now I see people as they really are." (Mark 8:22-25)

Ask Jesus to touch you so that you can see people as they really are.

People are ...
the crown of God's
creation.

GOD MADE PEOPLE TO GLORIFY HIM

DO THEY? HOW?

People are... not always what they seem to be.

People may look happy

but be very sad inside

People may look healthy

but be very sick inside

People may seem Christian

but not know Jesus at all

PEOPLE ENTERTAIN EACH OTHER. THANK YOU, GOD, FOR MAKING PEOPLE.

PEOPLE HELP EACH OTHER. THANK YOU, GOD, FOR MAKING PEOPLE.

PEOPLE ARE ALIKE. PEOPLE ARE DIFFERENT.

PEOPLE ARE INTERESTING. THANK YOU, GOD, FOR MAKING PEOPLE.

PEOPLE ARE TEACHERS. PEOPLE ARE LEARNERS.

PEOPLE NEED EACH OTHER. THANK YOU, GOD, FOR MAKING PEOPLE.

PEOPLE ARE FUN. THANK YOU, GOD, FOR MAKING PEOPLE.

THANK YOU, GOD, FOR MAKING PEOPLE.

PEOPLE HURT EACH OTHER. THANK YOU, GOD, FOR MAKING PEOPLE.

THANK YOU, GOD, FOR MAKING PEOPLE.

THANK YOU, GOD, FOR MAKING PEOPLE.

PEOPLE ARE HUMAN. THANK YOU, GOD, FOR MAKING PEOPLE.

THANK YOU, GOD, FOR MAKING PEOPLE.

Some people are hard to live with, and some people are hard to live without. But no matter who comes into our lives or whom God takes out of our lives, He has a purpose in it and will turn it into good for us.

THANK YOU, GOD, FOR MAKING PEOPLE

People are...all in need of love.

Tall people and small people need love.
Old people and young people need love.
People who have many things need love.
People who don't have much need love.
People who know a lot need love.
People who don't know very much need love
People we like need love.
People we don't like need love.

Love is:

patient ♥ kind ♥ gentle
never jealous ♥ never rude
not selfish ♥ never bragging
faithful ♥ truthful
not returning evil for evil
never demanding its own way

God said real love is being these
things even to people we don't like.

God wants us to love all people.

It's easy to love people we **liKe**.

like (līk) *v.* to be
pleased with or to
agree with, to enjoy,
to approve, to prefer.

It's hard to love people we don't liKe,
but God can help us love them.

Sometimes it helps
to get to know them better.

Write a biography of someone you don't like

biography (bī·ŏg′rȧ·fē) n.
the true story of another
person's life.

Find out:

who the people are in that person's family
that person's favorite things
some things that person doesn't like
things that make that person angry
sad things that have happened to that person
exciting things that person has done
things that person can do well
places that person has been
places that person would like to go
anything else you might think important

Find out these things from that person himself...

...or else from someone who loves him.

A BIOGRAPHY

(OF SOMEONE I DON'T LIKE)

WITH CRAYONS OR FELT PENS DRAW AS MANY DIFFERENT
SHAPES OF PEOPLE AS YOU CAN. USE A DIFFERENT COLOR FOR
EACH SHAPE.

IS THE PURPLE ANY BETTER THAN THE GREEN?

God made each of us a separate person. He also makes us members of Himself through Jesus Christ, our Savior. Jesus lives in us, so that makes each of us a little part of each other. For a little while let God help you...

...be
somebody
else

Imagine yourself as tall as that person.
Look at a situation the way that person
    might see it.
Think of yourself living in that person's house.
Think of yourself living in that person's skin.
Feel the sun and the rain the way that
    person might feel it.
How does it feel to have that person's
    responsibilities?
How does it feel to be called the things
    that person is called?
How does it look through that person's eyes?
What does the music sound like to that person?
Who is God to that person?
What does "too much" or "too little" mean
    to that person?
How does it feel to look like that person?
How does it feel to be that person?
                Is it fun sometimes?
                Is it scary sometimes?
                Does it hurt sometimes?

People are ... on their way

to heaven

or hell

WHERE ARE YOU GOING?